Judith N. Parsons

MATH·A·RIDDLE II

Secret-message challenges
to build basic skills
in multiplication

A FEARON MAKEMASTER® BOOK
Fearon Pitman Publishers, Inc.
Belmont, California

Edited by Gail Larrick
Designed by Paul Quin
Art drawn by Judith N. Parsons

ISBN-0-8224-4434-8
Printed in the United States of America.
1.9 8 7 6 5 4 3 2 1

CONTENTS

INTRODUCTION

About Math·A·Riddle II

Most teachers agree that pupils need considerably more practice with multiplication skills than is provided in the standard texts, especially *controlled drill* in manipulating the multiplication tables. By controlling the nature and sequence of the mathematical operations that pupils are asked to perform, and by providing opportunities for sufficient practice, teachers can help most pupils attain acceptable levels of speed and accuracy in this essential skill area.

Math·A·Riddle II has been designed to provide the controlled practice necessary for pupils to master the use of the multipliers 2 through 9. The exercises are carefully sequenced so as to minimize pupil confusion and facilitate rapid learning. Each exercise focuses pupil attention on the use of a single multiplier with both smaller and larger numbers. The emphasis throughout is upon mastery of one multiplier at a time. Mastery is measured in terms of both accuracy and speed.

Most teachers will also agree that it is relatively easy to provide problems for practice, but much harder to provide effective motivation. Math·A·Riddle provides that motivation in several ways:

□ Most children like puzzles, secrets, and secret codes. Sheet B in each Math·A·Riddle exercise contains a "secret message" that can be discovered only if the pupil has the proper "key" to unlock the "code." The key to the code can be obtained only by first correctly solving the math problems on Sheet A of that exercise and then using the left-to-right sequence of correct answers as the basis for unscrambling the secret message on Sheet B. Pupils feel a real sense of accomplishment when they have solved a Math·A·Riddle message and can tell it to their friends.

□ Children like some competition. Most pupils are eager to solve the math problems quickly and correctly so they can be first to decode the secret message.

□ Most children like riddles. Each message is a riddle, containing both question and answer. Once a pupil has decoded the secret message, he or she has a riddle that can be passed on to friends and family. This provides additional motivation for pupils to solve the code.

□ Children like silly puns, humor, and jokes of all kinds. The riddles in *Math·A·Riddle II* contain puns or jokes that generally appeal to eight- to twelve-year-olds.

The easy-to-duplicate MAKEMASTER® format of the Math·A·Riddle books makes this practice and motivation readily available to all of your students. So that you can easily locate and reduplicate pages as necessary, it is recommended you keep sheets removed from the book in a three-ring binder. In most classrooms Math·A·Riddle has been used as a large-group activity within the Regular math program. Some teachers have used all of the Math·A·Riddle exercises as the principal instructional tool for teaching multiplication. These teachers have generally begun with the "Number Fact Review for multiplication by 2" and have followed the teaching sequence outlined in the Math·A·Riddle table of contents. Other teachers have preferred to use some Math·A·Riddle exercises as class assignments to be graded and the remaining activity sheets as independent tasks to be done during slack times in the pupils' workday. A few teachers have used Math·A·Riddle as a basis for setting up math learning stations for individualized instruction.

The Parts of the Math·A·Riddle System

The Math·A·Riddle system for teaching multiplication skills has four parts. A *Number Fact Review* is found on one sheet at the beginning of each set of materials; it is used to review the basic number facts associated with a particular single-digit multiplier. The *Time Test* that accompanies each Number Fact Review focuses pupils' attention on the double goals of accuracy and speed and helps them monitor their progress toward those goals. The *Problem Sets* (each composed of one Sheet A and one Sheet B) are the heart of Math·A·Riddle; they provide practice and the secret-message motivator. The *Answer Sheets* are used with the Problem Sets to check answers before children attempt to decode the secret messages.

All parts of the Math·A·Riddle system are designed to be used *together,* in a pattern that has proven to be both highly enjoyable for students and effective in building skills. In order to get the most possible out of the Math·A·Riddle system, please read the remainder of this introduction carefully before introducing any Math·A·Riddle activity sheets to the class.

The Number Fact Review Sheet

In *Math·A·Riddle II,* this sheet contains exercises that help the pupil organize what he or she has previously learned about multiplication and establish the proper

mental set of the Time Test and Problem Sets that follow. Each of the duplicatable pages (8, 14, 24, 34, 42, 52, 62, and 70) contains the Number Fact Review exercises for one skill section. Pupils may be asked to take these review sheets home for study and practice. Or, use them as the basis for in-class verbal drill, with each student drilling and being drilled by a partner. Most teachers find it best to use these exercises for self-study or for partner work rather than for a large-group directed lesson, since the emphasis is on rapid manipulation of the number combinations.

The Time Tests and Problem Sets

The Time Tests (eight of them) are used integrally with the Problem Sets. In themselves they constitute a speed- and accuracy-building exercise; they also help pupils monitor their own progress. Most pupils like the challenge that these tests provide and take pride in measuring personal improvement on them. Experience indicates that nearly all pupils do achieve progress on the Time Tests, and that most pupils achieve mastery (100 percent accuracy within three minutes).

Math·A·Riddle is most successful when each test is used once with each Problem Set in a particular skill section. (Thus each test is used two or three times.) Prepare for the use of the tests and the Problem Sets by making a large Time Test Chart for your bulletin board.

*42 problems in 3 minutes	Time Test Chart Multiplication					
Multiplication	x 2	x3	x4	x5		
Mary Adams	*	*	*	*	*	
David Baca	*	*		*		

Be sure the chart is large enough for pupils to see from their seats. You will find pupils looking at it from time to time, particularly as they prepare to take the Time Tests.

Buy three boxes of foil stars—a box of red stars, one of silver, and one of gold—or have felt-tip pens of three different colors available. In order to complete one skill section, you will need to reproduce two or three copies of the Time Test and one copy of each

Problem Set for every pupil in your class, plus a few extras.

Use the Time Tests as follows:

1 *At the same time* that you pass out Sheet A of a Problem Set, pass out one copy of the Time Test that goes along with it.

2 Ask pupils to turn the Time Test sheet face down on top of their desks. Sheet A should remain face up.

3 Tell pupils that they will have three minutes to do the Time Test. Those who finish before the three minutes are up may begin doing Sheet A of the Problem Set right away—they need not wait.

4 When pupils are ready say, "When I say 'Begin,' turn your Time Test papers over and start to work. Work rapidly and carefully. Try to finish all the problems. Ready? Begin."

5 At the end of three minutes, say "Stop! Pupils who have finished all the problems please stand, and I will collect your test papers. Those pupils who did *not* finish the Time Test should put their test papers in their desks. Take the unfinished test paper home tonight and study it. You will have another chance to try the Time Test soon. Now, everybody please begin doing Sheet A."

6 While pupils are working the problems on Sheet A, check the completed Time Test sheets. Check each test paper *only* until you find an error. Circle the error and return the paper to the pupil for further study.

7 Each pupil who answers all test problems correctly in the three-minute test period should paste a star (or make a mark) after his or her name on the Time Test Chart.

The goal is for pupils to get 100 percent on each Time Test, three times in a row. The first time a pupil gets 100 percent on a test, he or she pastes a red star on the chart. The second 100 percent success on the same test warrants a silver star, and the third, a gold star. (The sample chart above shows that two pupils have taken the Time Test for multiplication by 2. Mary Adams got 100 percent three times. After her name are pasted a red star, a silver star, and a gold star. David Baca got 100 percent two times. He earned a red star and a silver star.)

You may wish to give pupils more than three chances to earn 100 percent on any given Time Test.

Introducing the First Problem Set

The procedure of the Time Test leading directly into work with Sheet A of a Problem Set is the standard one to follow after pupils have become familiar with Math·A·Riddle. But either before or after the first Time Test is given, you'll need to give students some general directions for doing Sheet A and for using the answers on it to decode the secret message found on the corresponding Sheet B. Make sure you have enough copies of each of these activity sheets for each pupil, plus a few extras. Then:

1 Pass out only the copies of Sheet A, along with the Time Test. *Keep the copies of Sheet B at your desk.* (When Sheet B is passed out with Sheet A of a set, children guess at the puzzle and try to use the numbers from Sheet B as answers to the problems on Sheet A.)

2 Have pupils work the problems on Sheet A. Ask pupils to work rapidly but carefully. Explain that they will need to have *all* the answers correct in order to decode the secret-message page, which you will pass out in a few minutes.

3 Check the answers using copies of the appropriate Answer Sheet. It is important that the answers on Sheet A be checked as soon as the child has finished, or the excitement about doing the riddle puzzle may dissipate. You, an aide, or another child should check the answers, or else each child should check his or her answers against the Answer Sheet at your desk. If a child has done more than two problems incorrectly, you'll usually want him or her to redo those problems. But even if you do not have the child redo the incorrect problems, make sure he or she writes in the correct answers to them.

Do not pass out Sheet B of the set until you are sure that all problems have been checked and the correct answers written in on Sheet A. (Remind your pupils that answers to the checking problems on Sheet A are not to be used when solving the riddle puzzle. Pupils should use only the answers to the problems that appear in columns headed with a letter of the alphabet. These columns are printed in a distinctive type and easily distinguishable from the checking problems. Problem Sets 6 through 27 do not have any checking problems.)

4 Pass out Sheet B of the set. Be sure that every child has copies of both the completed Sheet A and the corresponding Sheet B on the desk in front of him or her. Right-handed children should have Sheet A on the left and the Sheet B on the right; left-handed children will usually want to use the reverse arrangement.

5 Say, "Look first at your Sheet A. Put the index finger of one hand on the answer to problem A on line one. See what the number is. Now look at Sheet B, the puzzle sheet. Find the number that is the same as the answer to problem A, line one on Sheet A (The answer you have your finger on). A word is printed above the number. This is the first word of the riddle. Write this word on the top line of Sheet B.

"Now look at Sheet A again. Put your finger on the answer to problem B, line one. Notice the number in the answer. Look again at the puzzle sheet. Find the same number there. Do you see the word printed above this number? Write it at the top of the page—right after the word you wrote before. Now you have the second word of the riddle.

"Use each answer on Sheet A to find the clues to the secret-riddle message on Sheet B. Remember to follow the Sheet A answers in order—problems A, B, and C on line one, then problems A, B, and C on line two, and so on, until you have written the whole secret message."

6 Say, "Remember, use only the answers to the problems in the columns headed with a letter of the alphabet. Don't use the answers to the checking problems."

7 Let the children continue working by themselves. Any child who has difficulty with the decoding procedure should raise a hand and ask for your help.

8 Let pupils who wish to do so color the picture on their completed Sheet B.

You will find that your pupils are quick to understand the procedure for solving the Math·A·Riddle secret messages. After the first controlled session many teachers prefer to give out copies of Sheet B to individual children as soon as they have correctly completed the Sheet A problems. Often seeing the riddle page in the hands of another will motivate a pupil to finish his or her Sheet A more quickly.

And, finally, you will find that your pupils enjoy laughing about the riddles. Take time to laugh with them. Discuss the meanings of the puns with those pupils who do not quite understand them. Remember that much of the motivation for Math·A·Riddle is in the humor. Take time to enjoy it with the children.

Math Skill Sheets

Number Fact Review (2)

Fold part A of the paper back and turn the paper over, so all you can see is column A. Study the multiplication facts in column A. When you know them, turn the paper over so you cannot see column A. See how quickly you can work the problems in column B. Unfold the paper to check your answers. Now fold column A so that it covers column B. Do the problems in column C. Unfold again to check your answers. Finally do the problems in column D and check them to finish your practice.

A	B	C	D
$2 \times 0 = 0$	$2 \times 0 =$ ___	$2 \times 0 =$ ___	$2 \times 7 =$ ___
$2 \times 1 = 2$	$2 \times 1 =$ ___	$2 \times 1 =$ ___	$2 \times 4 =$ ___
$2 \times 2 = 4$	$2 \times 2 =$ ___	$2 \times 2 =$ ___	$2 \times 6 =$ ___
$2 \times 3 = 6$	$2 \times 3 =$ ___	$2 \times 3 =$ ___	$2 \times 3 =$ ___
$2 \times 4 = 8$	$2 \times 4 =$ ___	$2 \times 4 =$ ___	$2 \times 2 =$ ___
$2 \times 5 = 10$	$2 \times 5 =$ ___	$2 \times 5 =$ ___	$2 \times 8 =$ ___
$2 \times 6 = 12$	$2 \times 6 =$ ___	$2 \times 6 =$ ___	$2 \times 5 =$ ___
$2 \times 7 = 14$	$2 \times 7 =$ ___	$2 \times 7 =$ ___	$2 \times 9 =$ ___
$2 \times 8 = 16$	$2 \times 8 =$ ___	$2 \times 8 =$ ___	$2 \times 0 =$ ___
$2 \times 9 = 18$	$2 \times 9 =$ ___	$2 \times 9 =$ ___	$2 \times 1 =$ ___
$2 \times 10 = 20$	$2 \times 10 =$ ___	$2 \times 10 =$ ___	$2 \times 8 =$ ___

- - - - - - - - - - - - - - - - - - fold - - - - - - - - - - - - - - -

$$\begin{array}{r} 1 \\ \times\ 2 \\ \hline \end{array} \qquad \begin{array}{r} 6 \\ \times\ 2 \\ \hline \end{array} \qquad \begin{array}{r} 2 \\ \times\ 2 \\ \hline \end{array} \qquad \begin{array}{r} 5 \\ \times\ 2 \\ \hline \end{array} \qquad \begin{array}{r} 4 \\ \times\ 2 \\ \hline \end{array} \qquad \begin{array}{r} 0 \\ \times\ 2 \\ \hline \end{array}$$

$$\begin{array}{r} 3 \\ \times\ 2 \\ \hline \end{array} \qquad \begin{array}{r} 2 \\ \times\ 2 \\ \hline \end{array} \qquad \begin{array}{r} 9 \\ \times\ 2 \\ \hline \end{array} \qquad \begin{array}{r} 6 \\ \times\ 2 \\ \hline \end{array} \qquad \begin{array}{r} 8 \\ \times\ 2 \\ \hline \end{array} \qquad \begin{array}{r} 7 \\ \times\ 2 \\ \hline \end{array}$$

$$\begin{array}{r} 9 \\ \times\ 2 \\ \hline \end{array} \qquad \begin{array}{r} 5 \\ \times\ 2 \\ \hline \end{array} \qquad \begin{array}{r} 7 \\ \times\ 2 \\ \hline \end{array} \qquad \begin{array}{r} 8 \\ \times\ 2 \\ \hline \end{array} \qquad \begin{array}{r} 6 \\ \times\ 2 \\ \hline \end{array} \qquad \begin{array}{r} 0 \\ \times\ 2 \\ \hline \end{array}$$

$$\begin{array}{r} 2 \\ \times\ 2 \\ \hline \end{array} \qquad \begin{array}{r} 8 \\ \times\ 2 \\ \hline \end{array} \qquad \begin{array}{r} 5 \\ \times\ 2 \\ \hline \end{array} \qquad \begin{array}{r} 9 \\ \times\ 2 \\ \hline \end{array} \qquad \begin{array}{r} 3 \\ \times\ 2 \\ \hline \end{array} \qquad \begin{array}{r} 6 \\ \times\ 2 \\ \hline \end{array}$$

$$\begin{array}{r} 7 \\ \times\ 2 \\ \hline \end{array} \qquad \begin{array}{r} 9 \\ \times\ 2 \\ \hline \end{array} \qquad \begin{array}{r} 1 \\ \times\ 2 \\ \hline \end{array} \qquad \begin{array}{r} 4 \\ \times\ 2 \\ \hline \end{array} \qquad \begin{array}{r} 8 \\ \times\ 2 \\ \hline \end{array} \qquad \begin{array}{r} 3 \\ \times\ 2 \\ \hline \end{array}$$

$$\begin{array}{r} 4 \\ \times\ 2 \\ \hline \end{array} \qquad \begin{array}{r} 8 \\ \times\ 2 \\ \hline \end{array} \qquad \begin{array}{r} 6 \\ \times\ 2 \\ \hline \end{array} \qquad \begin{array}{r} 9 \\ \times\ 2 \\ \hline \end{array} \qquad \begin{array}{r} 7 \\ \times\ 2 \\ \hline \end{array} \qquad \begin{array}{r} 5 \\ \times\ 2 \\ \hline \end{array}$$

$$\begin{array}{r} 0 \\ \times\ 2 \\ \hline \end{array} \qquad \begin{array}{r} 9 \\ \times\ 2 \\ \hline \end{array} \qquad \begin{array}{r} 4 \\ \times\ 2 \\ \hline \end{array} \qquad \begin{array}{r} 5 \\ \times\ 2 \\ \hline \end{array} \qquad \begin{array}{r} 8 \\ \times\ 2 \\ \hline \end{array} \qquad \begin{array}{r} 3 \\ \times\ 2 \\ \hline \end{array}$$

Name_____ Time _____

Check each multiplication problem by addition.
Then use the products in columns A, B, and C to find your riddle.

	A		B		C	

1

$\begin{array}{r} 35 \\ \times\ 2 \\ \hline \end{array}$ $\longrightarrow$ $\begin{array}{r} 35 \\ +\ 35 \\ \hline \end{array}$

$\begin{array}{r} 79 \\ \times\ 2 \\ \hline \end{array}$ $\begin{array}{r} 79 \\ +\ 79 \\ \hline \end{array}$

$\begin{array}{r} 86 \\ \times\ 2 \\ \hline \end{array}$ $\begin{array}{r} 86 \\ +\ 86 \\ \hline \end{array}$

2

$\begin{array}{r} 105 \\ \times\ 2 \\ \hline \end{array}$ $\begin{array}{r} 105 \\ +\ 105 \\ \hline \end{array}$

$\begin{array}{r} 112 \\ \times\ 2 \\ \hline \end{array}$ $\begin{array}{r} 112 \\ +\ 112 \\ \hline \end{array}$

$\begin{array}{r} 408 \\ \times\ 2 \\ \hline \end{array}$ $\begin{array}{r} 408 \\ +\ 408 \\ \hline \end{array}$

3

$\begin{array}{r} 426 \\ \times\ 2 \\ \hline \end{array}$ $\begin{array}{r} 426 \\ +\ 426 \\ \hline \end{array}$

$\begin{array}{r} 803 \\ \times\ 2 \\ \hline \end{array}$ $\begin{array}{r} 803 \\ +\ 803 \\ \hline \end{array}$

$\begin{array}{r} 435 \\ \times\ 2 \\ \hline \end{array}$ $\begin{array}{r} 435 \\ +\ 435 \\ \hline \end{array}$

4

$\begin{array}{r} 620 \\ \times\ 2 \\ \hline \end{array}$ $\begin{array}{r} 620 \\ +\ 620 \\ \hline \end{array}$

$\begin{array}{r} 222 \\ \times\ 2 \\ \hline \end{array}$ $\begin{array}{r} 222 \\ +\ 222 \\ \hline \end{array}$

$\begin{array}{r} 208 \\ \times\ 2 \\ \hline \end{array}$ $\begin{array}{r} 208 \\ +\ 208 \\ \hline \end{array}$

5

$\begin{array}{r} 598 \\ \times\ 2 \\ \hline \end{array}$ $\begin{array}{r} 598 \\ +\ 598 \\ \hline \end{array}$

$\begin{array}{r} 473 \\ \times\ 2 \\ \hline \end{array}$ $\begin{array}{r} 473 \\ +\ 473 \\ \hline \end{array}$

$\begin{array}{r} 202 \\ \times\ 2 \\ \hline \end{array}$ $\begin{array}{r} 202 \\ +\ 202 \\ \hline \end{array}$

6

$\begin{array}{r} 321 \\ \times\ 2 \\ \hline \end{array}$ $\begin{array}{r} 321 \\ +\ 321 \\ \hline \end{array}$

$\begin{array}{r} 238 \\ \times\ 2 \\ \hline \end{array}$ $+$

$\begin{array}{r} 300 \\ \times\ 2 \\ \hline \end{array}$

Name _____

Riddle:

642
a

1,196
darling

224
Bigger

172
bigger,

870
baby

158
is

416
The

404
is

444
Answer:

70
Who

1,606
darling

476
little

852
her

210
Mrs.

600
Bigger.

946
baby

816
or

1,240
boy?

Name

Check each multiplication problem by addition.
Then use the products in columns A, B, and C to find your riddle.

	A	B	C

1

$$\begin{array}{r} 425 \\ \times\ 2 \\ \hline \end{array} \qquad +\ \begin{array}{r} 425 \\ 425 \\ \hline \end{array}$$

$$\begin{array}{r} 831 \\ \times\ 2 \\ \hline \end{array} \qquad +\ \begin{array}{r} 831 \\ 831 \\ \hline \end{array}$$

$$\begin{array}{r} 623 \\ \times\ 2 \\ \hline \end{array} \qquad +\ \begin{array}{r} 623 \\ 623 \\ \hline \end{array}$$

2

$$\begin{array}{r} 827 \\ \times\ 2 \\ \hline \end{array} \qquad +\ \begin{array}{r} 827 \\ 827 \\ \hline \end{array}$$

$$\begin{array}{r} 553 \\ \times\ 2 \\ \hline \end{array} \qquad +\ \begin{array}{r} 553 \\ 553 \\ \hline \end{array}$$

$$\begin{array}{r} 654 \\ \times\ 2 \\ \hline \end{array} \qquad +\ \begin{array}{r} 654 \\ 654 \\ \hline \end{array}$$

3

$$\begin{array}{r} 975 \\ \times\ 2 \\ \hline \end{array} \qquad +\ \begin{array}{r} 975 \\ 975 \\ \hline \end{array}$$

$$\begin{array}{r} 436 \\ \times\ 2 \\ \hline \end{array} \qquad +\ \begin{array}{r} 436 \\ 436 \\ \hline \end{array}$$

$$\begin{array}{r} 762 \\ \times\ 2 \\ \hline \end{array} \qquad +\ \begin{array}{r} 762 \\ 762 \\ \hline \end{array}$$

4

$$\begin{array}{r} 342 \\ \times\ 2 \\ \hline \end{array} \qquad +\ \begin{array}{r} 342 \\ 342 \\ \hline \end{array}$$

$$\begin{array}{r} 864 \\ \times\ 2 \\ \hline \end{array} \qquad +\ \begin{array}{r} 864 \\ 864 \\ \hline \end{array}$$

$$\begin{array}{r} 531 \\ \times\ 2 \\ \hline \end{array} \qquad +\ \begin{array}{r} 531 \\ 531 \\ \hline \end{array}$$

5

$$\begin{array}{r} 349 \\ \times\ 2 \\ \hline \end{array} \qquad +\ \underline{\hspace{2cm}}$$

$$\begin{array}{r} 779 \\ \times\ 2 \\ \hline \end{array} \qquad +\ \underline{\hspace{2cm}}$$

$$\begin{array}{r} 667 \\ \times\ 2 \\ \hline \end{array} \qquad +\ \underline{\hspace{2cm}}$$

6

$$\begin{array}{r} 585 \\ \times\ 2 \\ \hline \end{array} \qquad +\ \underline{\hspace{2cm}}$$

$$\begin{array}{r} 473 \\ \times\ 2 \\ \hline \end{array} \qquad +\ \underline{\hspace{2cm}}$$

$$\begin{array}{r} 225 \\ \times\ 2 \\ \hline \end{array} \qquad \underline{\hspace{2cm}}$$

Name _____

Number Fact Review (3)

Fold part A of the paper back and turn the paper over, so all you can see is column A. Study the multiplication facts in column A. When you know them, turn the paper over so you cannot see column A. See how quickly you can work the problems in column B. Unfold the paper to check your answers. Now fold column A so that it covers column B. Do the problems in column C. Unfold again to check your answers. Finally do the problems in column D and check them to finish your practice.

A		B	C	D
$3 \times 0 = 0$		$3 \times 0 =$ ___	$3 \times 0 =$ ___	$3 \times 4 =$ ___
$3 \times 1 = 3$		$3 \times 1 =$ ___	$3 \times 1 =$ ___	$3 \times 6 =$ ___
$3 \times 2 = 6$		$3 \times 2 =$ ___	$3 \times 2 =$ ___	$3 \times 7 =$ ___
$3 \times 3 = 9$		$3 \times 3 =$ ___	$3 \times 3 =$ ___	$3 \times 3 =$ ___
$3 \times 4 = 12$		$3 \times 4 =$ ___	$3 \times 4 =$ ___	$3 \times 2 =$ ___
$3 \times 5 = 15$		$3 \times 5 =$ ___	$3 \times 5 =$ ___	$3 \times 8 =$ ___
$3 \times 6 = 18$		$3 \times 6 =$ ___	$3 \times 6 =$ ___	$3 \times 5 =$ ___
$3 \times 7 = 21$		$3 \times 7 =$ ___	$3 \times 7 =$ ___	$3 \times 9 =$ ___
$3 \times 8 = 24$		$3 \times 8 =$ ___	$3 \times 8 =$ ___	$3 \times 0 =$ ___
$3 \times 9 = 27$		$3 \times 9 =$ ___	$3 \times 9 =$ ___	$3 \times 1 =$ ___
$3 \times 10 = 30$		$3 \times 10 =$ ___	$3 \times 10 =$ ___	$3 \times 8 =$ ___

- - - - - - - - - - - - - - - - - - - fold - - - - - - - - - - - - - - - - - - -

14

$$\begin{array}{r} 7 \\ \times\ 3 \\ \hline \end{array} \qquad \begin{array}{r} 6 \\ \times\ 3 \\ \hline \end{array} \qquad \begin{array}{r} 9 \\ \times\ 3 \\ \hline \end{array} \qquad \begin{array}{r} 4 \\ \times\ 3 \\ \hline \end{array} \qquad \begin{array}{r} 6 \\ \times\ 3 \\ \hline \end{array} \qquad \begin{array}{r} 5 \\ \times\ 3 \\ \hline \end{array}$$

$$\begin{array}{r} 8 \\ \times\ 3 \\ \hline \end{array} \qquad \begin{array}{r} 3 \\ \times\ 3 \\ \hline \end{array} \qquad \begin{array}{r} 8 \\ \times\ 3 \\ \hline \end{array} \qquad \begin{array}{r} 2 \\ \times\ 3 \\ \hline \end{array} \qquad \begin{array}{r} 6 \\ \times\ 3 \\ \hline \end{array} \qquad \begin{array}{r} 0 \\ \times\ 3 \\ \hline \end{array}$$

$$\begin{array}{r} 9 \\ \times\ 3 \\ \hline \end{array} \qquad \begin{array}{r} 4 \\ \times\ 3 \\ \hline \end{array} \qquad \begin{array}{r} 5 \\ \times\ 3 \\ \hline \end{array} \qquad \begin{array}{r} 7 \\ \times\ 3 \\ \hline \end{array} \qquad \begin{array}{r} 4 \\ \times\ 3 \\ \hline \end{array} \qquad \begin{array}{r} 8 \\ \times\ 3 \\ \hline \end{array}$$

$$\begin{array}{r} 9 \\ \times\ 3 \\ \hline \end{array} \qquad \begin{array}{r} 6 \\ \times\ 3 \\ \hline \end{array} \qquad \begin{array}{r} 8 \\ \times\ 3 \\ \hline \end{array} \qquad \begin{array}{r} 2 \\ \times\ 3 \\ \hline \end{array} \qquad \begin{array}{r} 9 \\ \times\ 3 \\ \hline \end{array} \qquad \begin{array}{r} 5 \\ \times\ 3 \\ \hline \end{array}$$

$$\begin{array}{r} 7 \\ \times\ 3 \\ \hline \end{array} \qquad \begin{array}{r} 9 \\ \times\ 3 \\ \hline \end{array} \qquad \begin{array}{r} 8 \\ \times\ 3 \\ \hline \end{array} \qquad \begin{array}{r} 7 \\ \times\ 3 \\ \hline \end{array} \qquad \begin{array}{r} 3 \\ \times\ 3 \\ \hline \end{array} \qquad \begin{array}{r} 9 \\ \times\ 3 \\ \hline \end{array}$$

$$\begin{array}{r} 4 \\ \times\ 3 \\ \hline \end{array} \qquad \begin{array}{r} 6 \\ \times\ 3 \\ \hline \end{array} \qquad \begin{array}{r} 7 \\ \times\ 3 \\ \hline \end{array} \qquad \begin{array}{r} 3 \\ \times\ 3 \\ \hline \end{array} \qquad \begin{array}{r} 9 \\ \times\ 3 \\ \hline \end{array} \qquad \begin{array}{r} 5 \\ \times\ 3 \\ \hline \end{array}$$

$$\begin{array}{r} 8 \\ \times\ 3 \\ \hline \end{array} \qquad \begin{array}{r} 6 \\ \times\ 3 \\ \hline \end{array} \qquad \begin{array}{r} 4 \\ \times\ 3 \\ \hline \end{array} \qquad \begin{array}{r} 9 \\ \times\ 3 \\ \hline \end{array} \qquad \begin{array}{r} 3 \\ \times\ 3 \\ \hline \end{array} \qquad \begin{array}{r} 6 \\ \times\ 3 \\ \hline \end{array}$$

Name _____ Time _____

Check each multiplication problem by addition.
Then use the products in columns A, B, and C to find your riddle.

	A	B	C

1

A:
$$\begin{array}{r} 35 \\ \times\ 3 \\ \hline \end{array}$$
$$+\ \begin{array}{r} 35 \\ 35 \\ 35 \\ \hline \end{array}$$

B:
$$\begin{array}{r} 74 \\ \times\ 3 \\ \hline \end{array}$$
$$+\ \begin{array}{r} 74 \\ 74 \\ 74 \\ \hline \end{array}$$

C:
$$\begin{array}{r} 81 \\ \times\ 3 \\ \hline \end{array}$$
$$+\ \begin{array}{r} 81 \\ 81 \\ 81 \\ \hline \end{array}$$

2

A:
$$\begin{array}{r} 95 \\ \times\ 3 \\ \hline \end{array}$$
$$+\ \begin{array}{r} 95 \\ 95 \\ 95 \\ \hline \end{array}$$

B:
$$\begin{array}{r} 86 \\ \times\ 3 \\ \hline \end{array}$$
$$+\ \begin{array}{r} 86 \\ 86 \\ 86 \\ \hline \end{array}$$

C:
$$\begin{array}{r} 57 \\ \times\ 3 \\ \hline \end{array}$$
$$+\ \begin{array}{r} 57 \\ 57 \\ 57 \\ \hline \end{array}$$

3

A:
$$\begin{array}{r} 46 \\ \times\ 3 \\ \hline \end{array}$$
$$+\ \begin{array}{r} 46 \\ 46 \\ 46 \\ \hline \end{array}$$

B:
$$\begin{array}{r} 97 \\ \times\ 3 \\ \hline \end{array}$$
$$+\ \begin{array}{r} 97 \\ 97 \\ 97 \\ \hline \end{array}$$

C:
$$\begin{array}{r} 88 \\ \times\ 3 \\ \hline \end{array}$$
$$+\ \begin{array}{r} 88 \\ 88 \\ 88 \\ \hline \end{array}$$

4

A:
$$\begin{array}{r} 101 \\ \times\ 3 \\ \hline \end{array}$$
$$+\ \underline{\hspace{3em}}$$

B:
$$\begin{array}{r} 605 \\ \times\ 3 \\ \hline \end{array}$$
$$+\ \underline{\hspace{3em}}$$

C:
$$\begin{array}{r} 407 \\ \times\ 3 \\ \hline \end{array}$$
$$+\ \underline{\hspace{3em}}$$

5

A:
$$\begin{array}{r} 703 \\ \times\ 3 \\ \hline \end{array}$$
$$+\ \underline{\hspace{3em}}$$

B:
$$\begin{array}{r} 809 \\ \times\ 3 \\ \hline \end{array}$$
$$+\ \underline{\hspace{3em}}$$

C:
$$\begin{array}{r} 400 \\ \times\ 3 \\ \hline \end{array}$$
$$+\ \underline{\hspace{3em}}$$

6

A:
$$\begin{array}{r} 262 \\ \times\ 3 \\ \hline \end{array}$$
$$+\ \underline{\hspace{3em}}$$

B:
$$\begin{array}{r} 295 \\ \times\ 3 \\ \hline \end{array}$$
$$+\ \underline{\hspace{3em}}$$

C:
$$\begin{array}{r} 351 \\ \times\ 3 \\ \hline \end{array}$$
$$+\ \underline{\hspace{3em}}$$

Name_____

Riddle:

786
to

222
must

303
pencil?

285
do

243
you

264
your

1,200
have

2,427
just

171
the

885
use

1,815
Answer:

291
eats

138
baby

258
if

105
What

1,053
a pen.

2,109
will

1,221
You

Name

Check each multiplication problem by addition.
Then use the products in columns A, B, and C to find your riddle.

	A		B		C	

1

$\begin{array}{r}602 \\ \times\ 3 \\ \hline \end{array}$ $+\begin{array}{r}602 \\ 602 \\ 602 \\ \hline \end{array}$

$\begin{array}{r}414 \\ \times\ 3 \\ \hline \end{array}$ $+\begin{array}{r}414 \\ 414 \\ 414 \\ \hline \end{array}$

$\begin{array}{r}820 \\ \times\ 3 \\ \hline \end{array}$ $+\begin{array}{r}820 \\ 820 \\ 820 \\ \hline \end{array}$

2

$\begin{array}{r}463 \\ \times\ 3 \\ \hline \end{array}$ $+\begin{array}{r}463 \\ 463 \\ 463 \\ \hline \end{array}$

$\begin{array}{r}885 \\ \times\ 3 \\ \hline \end{array}$ $+\begin{array}{r}885 \\ 885 \\ 885 \\ \hline \end{array}$

$\begin{array}{r}909 \\ \times\ 3 \\ \hline \end{array}$ $+\begin{array}{r}909 \\ 909 \\ 909 \\ \hline \end{array}$

3

$\begin{array}{r}697 \\ \times\ 3 \\ \hline \end{array}$ $+\begin{array}{r}697 \\ 697 \\ 697 \\ \hline \end{array}$

$\begin{array}{r}408 \\ \times\ 3 \\ \hline \end{array}$ $+\ \underline{\qquad}$

$\begin{array}{r}333 \\ \times\ 3 \\ \hline \end{array}$ $+\ \underline{\qquad}$

4

$\begin{array}{r}802 \\ \times\ 3 \\ \hline \end{array}$ $+\ \underline{\qquad}$

$\begin{array}{r}988 \\ \times\ 3 \\ \hline \end{array}$ $+\ \underline{\qquad}$

$\begin{array}{r}206 \\ \times\ 3 \\ \hline \end{array}$ $+\ \underline{\qquad}$

5

$\begin{array}{r}980 \\ \times\ 3 \\ \hline \end{array}$ $+\ \underline{\qquad}$

$\begin{array}{r}687 \\ \times\ 3 \\ \hline \end{array}$ $+\ \underline{\qquad}$

$\begin{array}{r}571 \\ \times\ 3 \\ \hline \end{array}$ $+\ \underline{\qquad}$

6

$\begin{array}{r}758 \\ \times\ 3 \\ \hline \end{array}$ $+\ \underline{\qquad}$

$\begin{array}{r}902 \\ \times\ 3 \\ \hline \end{array}$ $+\ \underline{\qquad}$

$\begin{array}{r}1,007 \\ \times\ 3 \\ \hline \end{array}$ $+\ \underline{\qquad}$

Name _____

Riddle:

2,460
you

2,940
a

1,242
would

2,691
foot

2,727
eight-

2,274
knife?

618
carrying

1,224
giant

1,713
sharp

1,389
call

2,406
who

1,806
What

2,964
is

2,706
Answer:

2,061
large,

2,655
an

3,021
Sir!

999
butcher

Name

Check each multiplication problem by addition.
Then use the products in columns A, B, and C to find your riddle.

	A		B		C	

1

673
× 3
_____

673
673
+ → 673
_____

484
× 3
_____

484
484
+ 484
_____

619
× 3
_____

619
619
+ 619
_____

2

393
× 3
_____   + _____

582
× 3
_____   + _____

808
× 3
_____   + _____

3

734
× 3
_____   + _____

897
× 3
_____   + _____

360
× 3
_____   + _____

4

179
× 3
_____   + _____

809
× 3
_____   + _____

637
× 3
_____   + _____

5

372
× 3
_____   + _____

917
× 3
_____   + _____

762
× 3
_____   + _____

6

231
× 3
_____   + _____

756
× 3
_____   + _____

280
× 3
_____   + _____

Name _____

Riddle:

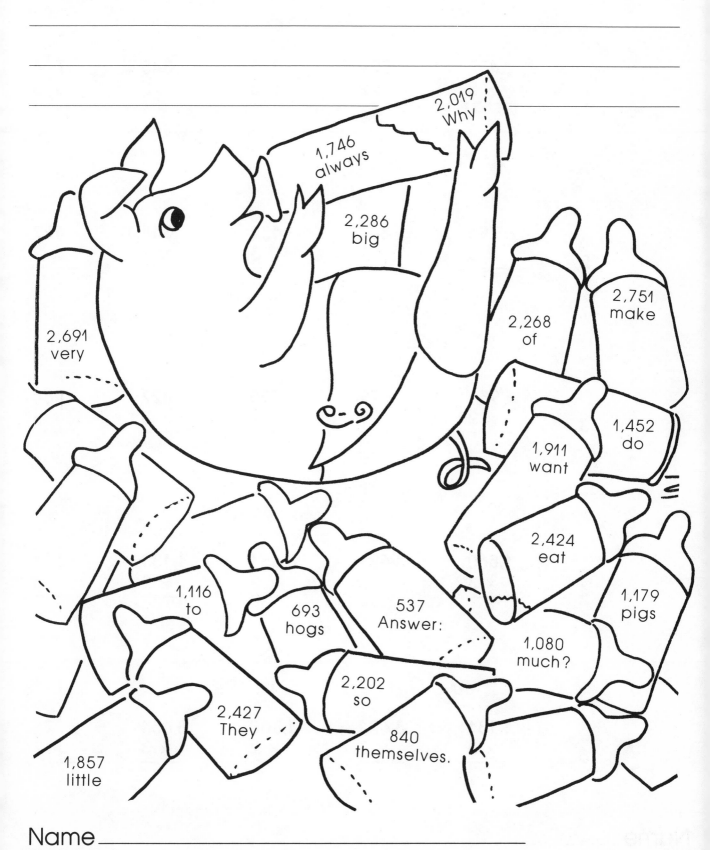

2,019
Why

1,746
always

2,286
big

2,268
of

2,751
make

2,691
very

1,911
want

1,452
do

2,424
eat

1,179
pigs

1,116
to

693
hogs

537
Answer:

1,080
much?

2,202
so

2,427
They

840
themselves.

1,857
little

Name

Use the products in columns A, B, C, D, and E to find your riddle.

	A	B	C	D	E
1	432 × 2	829 × 2	765 × 3	348 × 2	796 × 3
2	796 × 2	864 × 2	432 × 3	348 × 3	427 × 2
3	931 × 2	829 × 3	765 × 2	427 × 3	864 × 3
4	1,860 × 3	4,621 × 2	8,651 × 2	1,131 × 2	2,321 × 3
5	1,131 × 3	3,621 × 3	1,860 × 2	8,651 × 3	2,321 × 2

Name_____

Riddle: _____

_____

_____

_____

_____

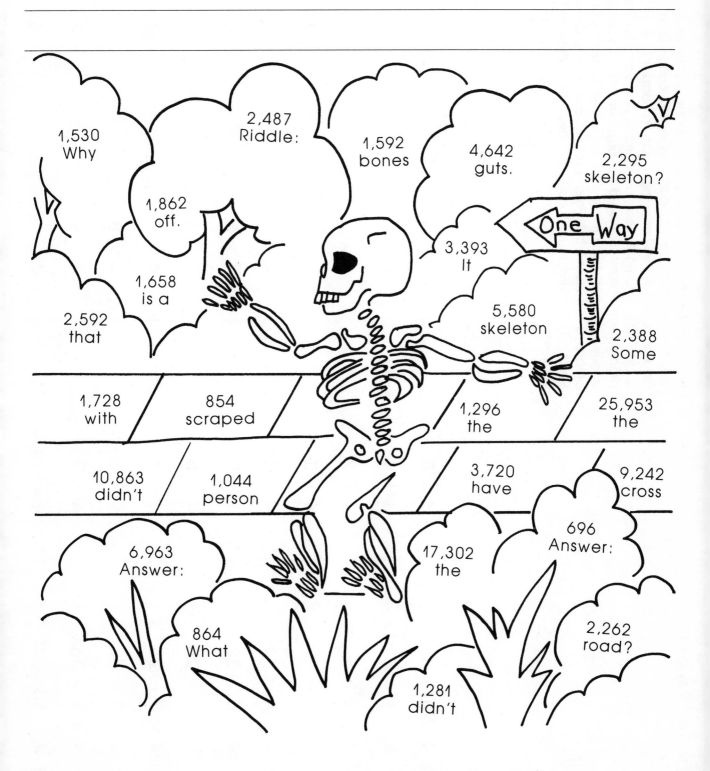

1,530
Why

2,487
Riddle:

1,592
bones

4,642
guts.

2,295
skeleton?

1,862
off.

1,658
is a

2,592
that

3,393
It

One Way

5,580
skeleton

2,388
Some

1,728
with

854
scraped

1,296
the

25,953
the

10,863
didn't

1,044
person

3,720
have

9,242
cross

6,963
Answer:

17,302
the

696
Answer:

864
What

2,262
road?

1,281
didn't

Name _____

Number Fact Review (4)

Fold part A of the paper back and turn the paper over, so all you can see is column A. Study the multiplication facts in column A. When you know them, turn the paper over so you cannot see column A. See how quickly you can work the problems in column B. Unfold the paper to check your answers. Now fold column A so that it covers column B. Do the problems in column C. Unfold again to check your answers. Finally do the problems in column D and check them to finish your practice.

A	B	C	D
$4 \times 0 = 0$	$4 \times 0 =$ ___	$4 \times 0 =$ ___	$4 \times 4 =$ ___
$4 \times 1 = 4$	$4 \times 1 =$ ___	$4 \times 1 =$ ___	$4 \times 6 =$ ___
$4 \times 2 = 8$	$4 \times 2 =$ ___	$4 \times 2 =$ ___	$4 \times 7 =$ ___
$4 \times 3 = 12$	$4 \times 3 =$ ___	$4 \times 3 =$ ___	$4 \times 3 =$ ___
$4 \times 4 = 16$	$4 \times 4 =$ ___	$4 \times 4 =$ ___	$4 \times 2 =$ ___
$4 \times 5 = 20$	$4 \times 5 =$ ___	$4 \times 5 =$ ___	$4 \times 8 =$ ___
$4 \times 6 = 24$	$4 \times 6 =$ ___	$4 \times 6 =$ ___	$4 \times 5 =$ ___
$4 \times 7 = 28$	$4 \times 7 =$ ___	$4 \times 7 =$ ___	$4 \times 9 =$ ___
$4 \times 8 = 32$	$4 \times 8 =$ ___	$4 \times 8 =$ ___	$4 \times 0 =$ ___
$4 \times 9 = 36$	$4 \times 9 =$ ___	$4 \times 9 =$ ___	$4 \times 1 =$ ___
$4 \times 10 = 40$	$4 \times 10 =$ ___	$4 \times 10 =$ ___	$4 \times 8 =$ ___

– – – – – – – – – – – – – – – – fold – – – – – – – – – – – – – – – – – –

5 × 4	1 × 4	7 × 4	2 × 4	9 × 4	5 × 4
8 × 4	3 × 4	5 × 4	7 × 4	8 × 4	6 × 4
9 × 4	0 × 4	8 × 4	4 × 4	9 × 4	3 × 4
6 × 4	9 × 4	3 × 4	6 × 4	0 × 4	4 × 4
7 × 4	8 × 4	5 × 4	8 × 4	7 × 4	6 × 4
9 × 4	3 × 4	4 × 4	9 × 4	7 × 4	5 × 4
4 × 4	7 × 4	9 × 4	6 × 4	8 × 4	3 × 4

Name _____ Time _____

Use the products in columns A, B, C, D, and E to find your riddle.

	A	B	C	D	E
1	206 × 4	321 × 4	211 × 4	704 × 4	12 × 4
2	340 × 4	462 × 4	837 × 4	916 × 4	618 × 4
3	921 × 4	210 × 4	998 × 4	786 × 4	821 × 4
4	372 × 4	467 × 4	1,241 × 4	896 × 4	2,165 × 4
5	2,079 × 4	397 × 4	8,291 × 4	725 × 4	885 × 4

Name_____

Riddle: _____

Name_____

Use the products in columns A, B, C, D, and E to find your riddle.

	A	B	C	D	E
1	279 × 4	897 × 4	725 × 4	832 × 4	979 × 4
2	826 × 4	932 × 4	756 × 4	829 × 4	997 × 4
3	5,251 × 4	8,695 × 4	7,653 × 4	7,651 × 4	9,265 × 4
4	8,297 × 4	3,021 × 4	9,112 × 4	8,012 × 4	1,765 × 4
5	9,721 × 4	3,256 × 4	3,321 × 4	9,769 × 4	5,572 × 4

Name_____

Riddle:

34,780
drip-

12,084
are

13,024
and-

37,060
Answer:

1,116
What

3,024
a

33,188
You

7,060
get a

21,004
a

38,884
wash-

39,076
(were-)

3,988
with

30,612
dry

2,900
you

3,728
cross

22,288
wolf.

30,604
suit?

3,328
get

3,588
do

3,316
monster

13,284
wear

3,916
when

32,048
to

3,304
you

36,448
sure

Name

Use the products in columns A, B, C, D, and E to find your riddle.

	A	B	C	D	E
1	739 × 4	829 × 4	906 × 4	821 × 4	665 × 4
2	9,821 × 4	7,652 × 4	5,561 × 4	3,215 × 4	9,652 × 4
3	5,081 × 4	87 × 4	6,321 × 4	6,921 × 4	8,679 × 4
4	3,765 × 4	8,276 × 4	6,937 × 4	1,826 × 4	9,523 × 4
5	8,295 × 4	7,658 × 4	3,219 × 4	8,665 × 4	4,493 × 4

Name _____

38,608 baseball

38,092 like

33,104 Answer:

22,244 get

27,684 the

12,860 a

25,284 in

2,956 Riddle:

3,316 Why

34,660 the

34,716 early

39,284 hard

20,324 game

7,304 bats

12,876 in

15,060 afternoon?

2,660 always

17,972 daytime.

30,608 to

27,748 Because

3,284 it

30,632 sleep

33,180 to

348 started

3,624 is

Name _____

Use the products in columns A, B, C, D, and E to find your riddle.

	A	B	C	D	E
1	469 × 4	873 × 3	352 × 2	1,876 × 4	6,321 × 2
2	578 × 4	352 × 4	469 × 3	1,876 × 2	578 × 3
3	6,321 × 4	1,876 × 3	873 × 4	352 × 3	578 × 2
4	1,897 × 4	469 × 2	6,321 × 3	873 × 2	5,621 × 4
5	5,621 × 3	8,690 × 4	1,957 × 3	8,690 × 3	1,957 × 4

Name_____

Riddle:

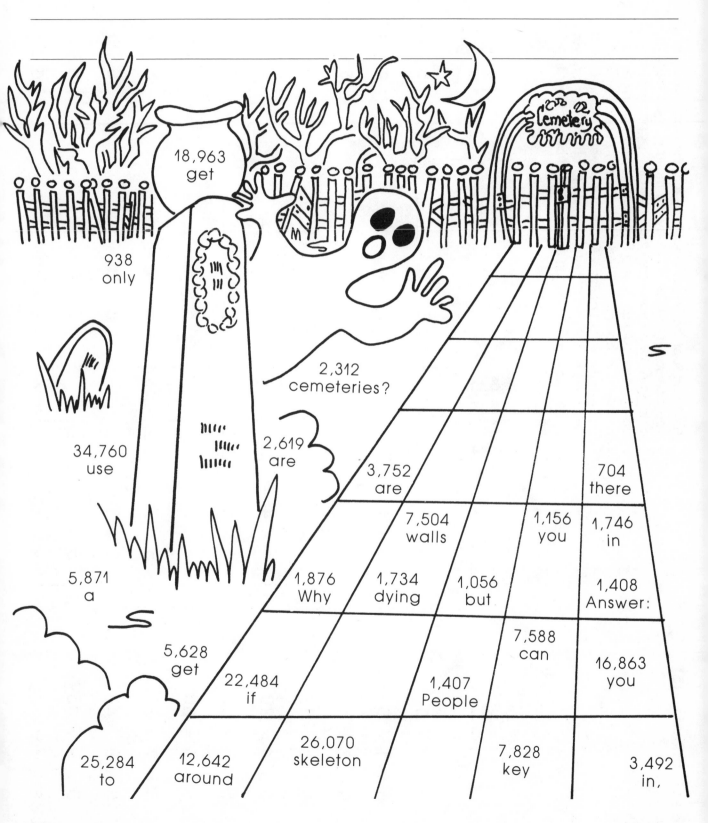

18,963
get

938
only

34,760
use

2,619
are

2,312
cemeteries?

3,752
are

704
there

7,504
walls

1,156
you

1,746
in

5,871
a

1,876
Why

1,734
dying

1,056
but

1,408
Answer:

5,628
get

7,588
can

16,863
you

22,484
if

1,407
People

25,284
to

12,642
around

26,070
skeleton

7,828
key

3,492
in,

Name

Number Fact Review (5)

Fold part A of the paper back and turn the paper over, so all you can see is column A. Study the multiplication facts in column A. When you know them, turn the paper over so you cannot see column A. See how quickly you can work the problems in column B. Unfold the paper to check your answers. Now fold column A so that it covers column B. Do the problems in column C. Unfold again to check your answers. Finally do the problems in column D and check them to finish your practice.

A		B		C		D	
5 × 0 = 0		5 × 0 = ___		5 × 0 = ___		5 × 4 = ___	
5 × 1 = 5		5 × 1 = ___		5 × 1 = ___		5 × 6 = ___	
5 × 2 = 10		5 × 2 = ___		5 × 2 = ___		5 × 7 = ___	
5 × 3 = 15		5 × 3 = ___		5 × 3 = ___		5 × 3 = ___	
5 × 4 = 20		5 × 4 = ___		5 × 4 = ___		5 × 2 = ___	
5 × 5 = 25		5 × 5 = ___		5 × 5 = ___		5 × 8 = ___	
5 × 6 = 30		5 × 6 = ___		5 × 6 = ___		5 × 5 = ___	
5 × 7 = 35		5 × 7 = ___		5 × 7 = ___		5 × 9 = ___	
5 × 8 = 40		5 × 8 = ___		5 × 8 = ___		5 × 0 = ___	
5 × 9 = 45		5 × 9 = ___		5 × 9 = ___		5 × 1 = ___	
5 × 10 = 50		5 × 10 = ___		5 × 10 = ___		5 × 8 = ___	

-- fold --

34

7 × 5	9 × 5	6 × 5	8 × 5	6 × 5	3 × 5
8 × 5	6 × 5	5 × 5	9 × 5	3 × 5	5 × 5
9 × 5	4 × 5	1 × 5	6 × 5	9 × 5	7 × 5
8 × 5	2 × 5	0 × 5	4 × 5	8 × 5	7 × 5
2 × 5	9 × 5	6 × 5	7 × 5	9 × 5	7 × 5
0 × 5	9 × 5	8 × 5	4 × 5	1 × 5	8 × 5
9 × 5	8 × 5	3 × 5	9 × 5	7 × 5	6 × 5

Name _____ Time _____

Use the products in columns A, B, C, D, and E to find your riddle.

	A	B	C	D	E
1	$98.20 × 5	$32.76 × 5	$1.75 × 5	$2.25 × 5	$37.21 × 5
2	$19.95 × 5	$23.45 × 5	$2.82 × 5	$27.62 × 5	$84.47 × 5
3	$3.95 × 5	$9.37 × 5	$43.02 × 5	$17.37 × 5	$8.21 × 5
4	$13.42 × 5	$27.76 × 5	$8.84 × 5	$99.90 × 5	$5.32 × 5
5	$1.87 × 5	$4.32 × 5	$56.90 × 5	$44.32 × 5	$97.36 × 5

Name_____

Riddle: _____

_____
_____
_____
_____

$422.35 run

$491.00 What

$486.80 puss.

$284.50 very

$138.80 He

$41.05 Answer:

$117.25 his

$46.85 by

$19.75 over

$14.10 cat

$44.20 just

$86.85 steamroller?

$163.80 did

$221.60 long

$9.35 with

$138.10 was

$11.25 man

$26.60 there

$186.05 say

$215.10 a

$99.75 when

$499.50 stood

$67.10 Nothing.

$21.60 a

$8.75 the

Name_____

Use the products in columns A, B, C, D, and E to find your riddle.

	A	B	C	D	E
1	$20.75 × 5	$10.94 × 5	$7.82 × 5	$12.35 × 5	$8.74 × 5
2	$9.65 × 5	$17.49 × 5	$43.29 × 5	$56.82 × 5	$47.36 × 5
3	$306.21 × 5	$475.02 × 5	$397.76 × 5	$421.21 × 5	$47.75 × 5
4	$896.32 × 5	$726.32 × 5	$43.75 × 5	$921.35 × 5	$87.73 × 5
5	$42.95 × 5	$137.60 × 5	$324.62 × 5	$921.70 × 5	$42.93 × 5

Name _____

Riddle:

Use the products in columns A, B, C, D, and E to find your riddle.

	A	B	C	D	E
1	$42.75 × 3	5,673 × 4	$27.85 × 5	$42.36 × 3	450 × 3
2	$27.82 × 5	837 × 4	456 × 3	$82.74 × 3	897 × 5
3	$42.35 × 5	$87.30 × 3	$27.62 × 4	813 × 3	$42.50 × 5
4	$82.64 × 3	930 × 5	426 × 3	$32.41 × 4	$82.50 × 5
5	4,197 × 3	$82.97 × 3	$42.56 × 4	$82.97 × 4	$32.95 × 5

Name_____

40

Riddle: _____

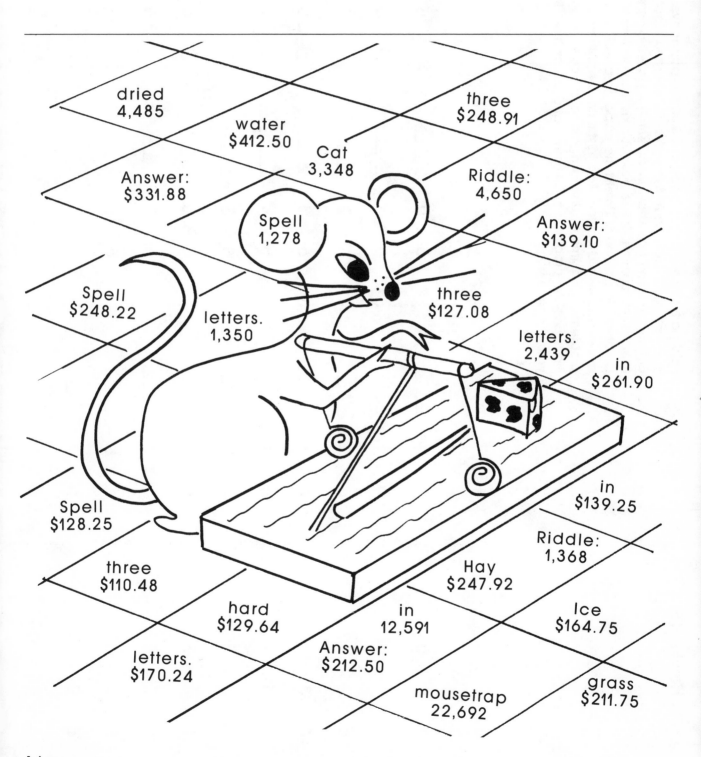

dried
4,485

water
$412.50

three
$248.91

Cat
3,348

Answer:
$331.88

Riddle:
4,650

Spell
1,278

Answer:
$139.10

Spell
$248.22

letters.
1,350

three
$127.08

letters.
2,439

in
$261.90

Spell
$128.25

in
$139.25

Riddle:
1,368

three
$110.48

Hay
$247.92

hard
$129.64

in
12,591

Ice
$164.75

Answer:
$212.50

letters.
$170.24

mousetrap
22,692

grass
$211.75

Name _____

Number Fact Review (6)

Fold part A of the paper back and turn the paper over, so all you can see is column A. Study the multiplication facts in column A. When you know them, turn the paper over so you cannot see column A. See how quickly you can work the problems in column B. Unfold the paper to check your answers. Now fold column A so that it covers column B. Do the problems in column C. Unfold again to check your answers. Finally do the problems in column D and check them to finish your practice.

A

$6 \times 0 = 0$

$6 \times 1 = 6$

$6 \times 2 = 12$

$6 \times 3 = 18$

$6 \times 4 = 24$

$6 \times 5 = 30$

$6 \times 6 = 36$

$6 \times 7 = 42$

$6 \times 8 = 48$

$8 \times 9 = 54$

$6 \times 10 = 60$

-------------------- fold --------------------

B

$6 \times 0 = \underline{\hspace{1cm}}$

$6 \times 1 = \underline{\hspace{1cm}}$

$6 \times 2 = \underline{\hspace{1cm}}$

$6 \times 3 = \underline{\hspace{1cm}}$

$6 \times 4 = \underline{\hspace{1cm}}$

$6 \times 5 = \underline{\hspace{1cm}}$

$6 \times 6 = \underline{\hspace{1cm}}$

$6 \times 7 = \underline{\hspace{1cm}}$

$6 \times 8 = \underline{\hspace{1cm}}$

$6 \times 9 = \underline{\hspace{1cm}}$

$6 \times 10 = \underline{\hspace{1cm}}$

C

$6 \times 0 = \underline{\hspace{1cm}}$

$6 \times 1 = \underline{\hspace{1cm}}$

$6 \times 2 = \underline{\hspace{1cm}}$

$6 \times 3 = \underline{\hspace{1cm}}$

$6 \times 4 = \underline{\hspace{1cm}}$

$6 \times 5 = \underline{\hspace{1cm}}$

$6 \times 6 = \underline{\hspace{1cm}}$

$6 \times 7 = \underline{\hspace{1cm}}$

$6 \times 8 = \underline{\hspace{1cm}}$

$6 \times 9 = \underline{\hspace{1cm}}$

$6 \times 10 = \underline{\hspace{1cm}}$

D

$6 \times 4 = \underline{\hspace{1cm}}$

$6 \times 6 = \underline{\hspace{1cm}}$

$6 \times 7 = \underline{\hspace{1cm}}$

$6 \times 3 = \underline{\hspace{1cm}}$

$6 \times 2 = \underline{\hspace{1cm}}$

$6 \times 8 = \underline{\hspace{1cm}}$

$6 \times 5 = \underline{\hspace{1cm}}$

$6 \times 9 = \underline{\hspace{1cm}}$

$6 \times 0 = \underline{\hspace{1cm}}$

$6 \times 1 = \underline{\hspace{1cm}}$

$6 \times 8 = \underline{\hspace{1cm}}$

5 × 6	7 × 6	8 × 6	6 × 6	7 × 6	3 × 6
9 × 6	4 × 6	5 × 6	8 × 6	6 × 6	9 × 6
2 × 6	7 × 6	6 × 6	9 × 6	5 × 6	0 × 6
7 × 6	8 × 6	3 × 6	8 × 6	5 × 6	7 × 6
9 × 6	6 × 6	3 × 6	2 × 6	7 × 6	4 × 6
9 × 6	5 × 6	8 × 6	6 × 6	9 × 6	8 × 6
5 × 6	7 × 6	6 × 6	3 × 6	9 × 6	8 × 6

Name_____ Time _____

Use the products in columns A, B, C, D, and E to find your riddle.

	A	B	C	D	E
1	435 × 6	821 × 6	403 × 6	62 × 6	837 × 6
2	395 × 6	219 × 6	897 × 6	432 × 6	824 × 6
3	306 × 6	695 × 6	437 × 6	893 × 6	47 × 6
4	829 × 6	37 × 6	849 × 6	366 × 6	749 × 6
5	882 × 6	754 × 6	865 × 6	973 × 6	826 × 6

Name _____

Riddle:

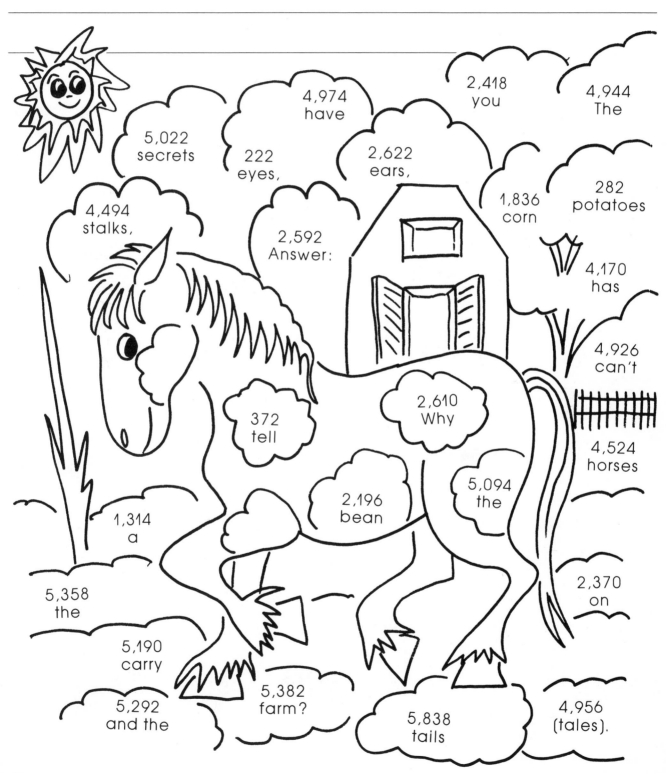

Name _____

Use the products in columns A, B, C, D, and E to find your riddle.

	A	B	C	D	E
1	$27.60 × 6	495 × 6	$37.42 × 6	897 × 6	487 × 6
2	$94.35 × 6	$78.45 × 6	$47.31 × 6	297 × 6	829 × 6
3	453 × 6	$69.76 × 6	466 × 6	$86.77 × 6	$33.95 × 6
4	$21.93 × 6	467 × 6	$36.60 × 6	457 × 6	769 × 6
5	$88.76 × 6	869 × 6	$37.82 × 6	$72.65 × 6	$56.98 × 6

Name _____

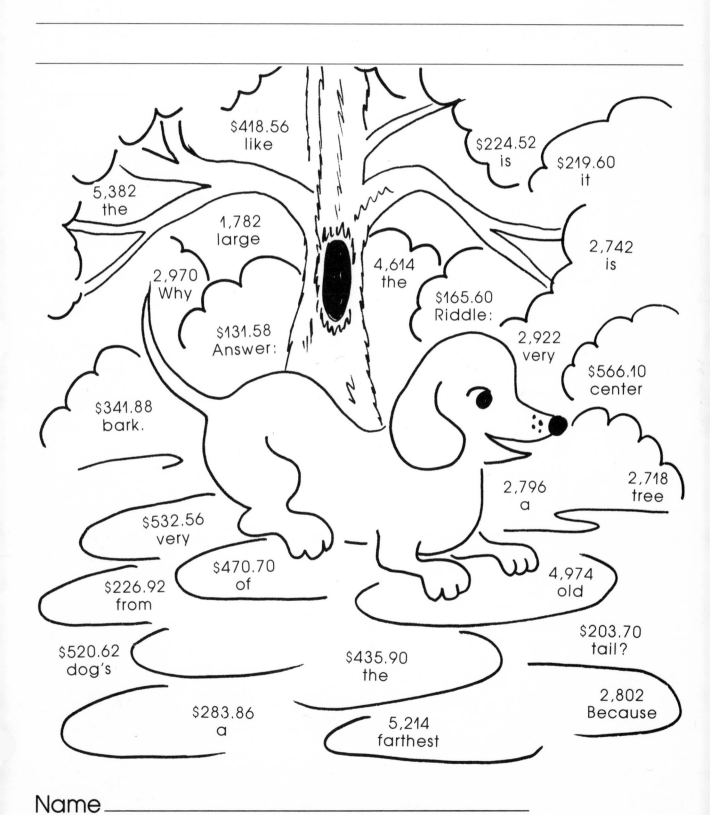

© 1979 Fearon Pitman Publishers, Inc.

Name

Use the products in columns A, B, C, D, and E to find your riddle.

	A	B	C	D	E
1	$456 × 6	$82.30 × 6	$67.95 × 6	209 × 6	$47.65 × 6
2	$27.70 × 6	$83.95 × 6	489 × 6	$93.46 × 6	$78.93 × 6
3	963 × 6	$84.95 × 6	$31.42 × 6	676 × 6	$33.68 × 6
4	$47.75 × 6	$93.87 × 6	$96.68 × 6	$73.89 × 6	995 × 6
5	837 × 6	$45.86 × 6	576 × 6	$49.98 × 6	$187.65 × 6

Name _____

Riddle:

4,056
Answer:

$285.90
Washington's

$188.52
first?

2,736
Why

$443.34
finished

$503.70
army

$275.16
March

$286.50
it

$560.76
very

$1,125.90
days.

3,456
of

5,970
a

$563.22
had

5,022
long

2,934
so

$166.20
large

1,254
George

$580.08
just

$509.70
April

$407.70
General

5,778
on

$473.58
tired

$299.88
thirty-one

$202.08
Because

$493.80
was

Name

Use the products in columns A, B, C, D, and E to find your riddle.

	A	B	C	D	E
1	$42.26 × 6	$18.07 × 3	$46.71 × 5	$25.82 × 4	$19.37 × 6
2	$37.82 × 6	$56.70 × 3	$91.87 × 4	1,276 × 6	$195.72 × 5
3	4,809 × 3	$31.25 × 6	2,091 × 4	$36.57 × 3	2,153 × 6
4	$176.05 × 6	$132.57 × 3	3,275 × 5	$176.20 × 4	2,576 × 6
5	4,031 × 3	$365.98 × 6	$498.76 × 4	3,297 × 6	$478.97 × 3

Name _____

$253.56
Riddle:

$978.60
the

$116.22
officers

$103.28
traffic

12,093
ton

16,375
up

19,782
one

$187.50
world?

8,364
Answer:

$54.21
Why

7,656
in

12,918
they

$233.55
are

14,427
whole

15,456
five-

$367.48
people

$170.10
strongest

$704.80
a

$226.92
the

$2,195.88
truck

$109.71
Because

$1,056.30
can

$397.71
hold

$1,995.04
with

$1,436.91
hand.

Name

Number Fact Review (7)

Fold part A of the paper back and turn the paper over, so all you can see is column A. Study the multiplication facts in column A. When you know them, turn the paper over so you cannot see column A. See how quickly you can work the problems in column B. Unfold the paper to check your answers. Now fold column A so that it covers column B. Do the problems in column C. Unfold again to check your answers. Finally do the problems in column D and check them to finish your practice.

A

$7 \times 0 = 0$

$7 \times 1 = 7$

$7 \times 2 = 14$

$7 \times 3 = 21$

$7 \times 4 = 28$

$7 \times 5 = 35$

$7 \times 6 = 42$

$7 \times 7 = 49$

$7 \times 8 = 56$

$7 \times 9 = 63$

$7 \times 10 = 70$

- - - - - - - - - - - - - fold - - - - - - - - - - - - -

B

$7 \times 0 =$ _____

$7 \times 1 =$ _____

$7 \times 2 =$ _____

$7 \times 3 =$ _____

$7 \times 4 =$ _____

$7 \times 5 =$ _____

$7 \times 6 =$ _____

$7 \times 7 =$ _____

$7 \times 8 =$ _____

$7 \times 9 =$ _____

$7 \times 10 =$ _____

C

$7 \times 0 =$ _____

$7 \times 1 =$ _____

$7 \times 2 =$ _____

$7 \times 3 =$ _____

$7 \times 4 =$ _____

$7 \times 5 =$ _____

$7 \times 6 =$ _____

$7 \times 7 =$ _____

$7 \times 8 =$ _____

$7 \times 9 =$ _____

$7 \times 10 =$ _____

D

$7 \times 4 =$ _____

$7 \times 6 =$ _____

$7 \times 7 =$ _____

$7 \times 3 =$ _____

$7 \times 2 =$ _____

$7 \times 8 =$ _____

$7 \times 5 =$ _____

$7 \times 9 =$ _____

$7 \times 0 =$ _____

$7 \times 1 =$ _____

$7 \times 8 =$ _____

5 × 7	4 × 7	6 × 7	5 × 7	8 × 7	7 × 7
9 × 7	7 × 7	5 × 7	8 × 7	6 × 7	3 × 7
9 × 7	4 × 7	3 × 7	8 × 7	6 × 7	9 × 7
7 × 7	5 × 7	2 × 7	6 × 7	5 × 7	4 × 7
7 × 7	3 × 7	9 × 7	0 × 7	4 × 7	7 × 7
9 × 7	5 × 7	6 × 7	8 × 7	3 × 7	9 × 7
5 × 7	8 × 7	4 × 7	6 × 7	7 × 7	2 × 7

Name _____ Time _____

53

Use the products in columns A, B, C, D, and E to find your riddle.

	A	B	C	D	E
1	309 × 7	178 × 7	467 × 7	801 × 7	63 × 7
2	810 × 7	463 × 7	987 × 7	365 × 7	907 × 7
3	462 × 7	879 × 7	605 × 7	798 × 7	978 × 7
4	789 × 7	657 × 7	769 × 7	869 × 7	557 × 7
5	498 × 7	689 × 7	709 × 7	487 × 7	777 × 7

Name _____

Riddle:

_____

_____

_____

Name _____

Use the products in columns A, B, C, D, and E to find your riddle.

	A	B	C	D	E
1	$27.65 × 7	$46.32 × 7	$21.98 × 7	$46.89 × 7	489 × 7
2	2,198 × 7	$32.78 × 7	$88.99 × 7	$38.65 × 7	$797.82 × 7
3	3,877 × 7	$97.65 × 7	$829.00 × 7	$452.50 × 7	7,789 × 7
4	$88.97 × 7	8,765 × 7	3,872 × 7	$487.73 × 7	2,903 × 7
5	8,956 × 7	$787.59 × 7	$376.50 × 7	$295.20 × 7	$365.10 × 7

Name _____

Riddle:

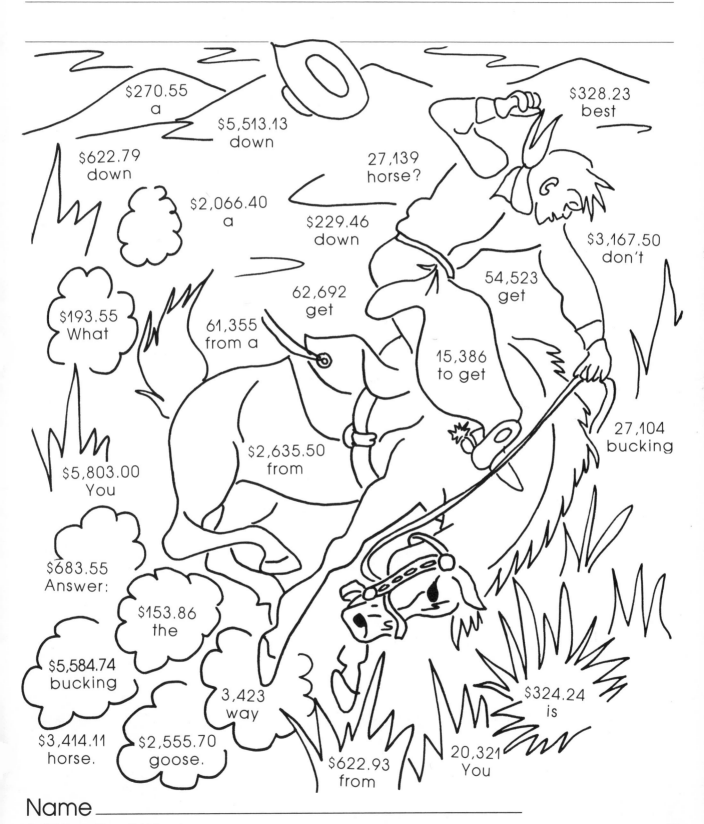

$270.55
a

$5,513.13
down

$622.79
down

$2,066.40
a

27,139
horse?

$229.46
down

$328.23
best

$3,167.50
don't

54,523
get

62,692
get

$193.55
What

61,355
from a

15,386
to get

27,104
bucking

$5,803.00
You

$2,635.50
from

$683.55
Answer:

$153.86
the

$5,584.74
bucking

3,423
way

$324.24
is

$3,414.11
horse.

$2,555.70
goose.

$622.93
from

20,321
You

Name _____

Use the products in columns A, B, C, D, and E to find your riddle.

	A	B	C	D	E
1	$675.21 × 7	$307.06 × 7	$278.35 × 7	$26.78 × 7	$392.70 × 7
2	4,621 × 7	$86.75 × 7	$895.56 × 7	$42.76 × 7	$165.32 × 7
3	$85.97 × 7	$965.82 × 7	4,398 × 7	$562.75 × 7	$31.89 × 7
4	$495.76 × 7	$382.89 × 7	$479.83 × 7	$556.72 × 7	3,821 × 7
5	$485.97 × 7	$321.56 × 7	4,872 × 7	44,582 × 7	$998.87 × 7

Name _____

Riddle:

_____

_____

_____

_____

Use the products in columns A, B, C, D, and E to find your riddle.

	A	B	C	D	E
1	42,765 × 6	21,325 × 7	3,760 × 3	4,257 × 4	32,625 × 2
2	$861.35 × 6	25,321 × 7	24,532 × 5	$675.21 × 3	3,025 × 7
3	4,637 × 4	$222.45 × 3	$356.27 × 7	22,450 × 6	22,761 × 7
4	35,671 × 4	$687.92 × 2	45,672 × 6	$21.67 × 7	$365.42 × 3
5	$810.76 × 7	$325.62 × 5	$42.86 × 3	21,235 × 6	$487.92 × 7

Name _____

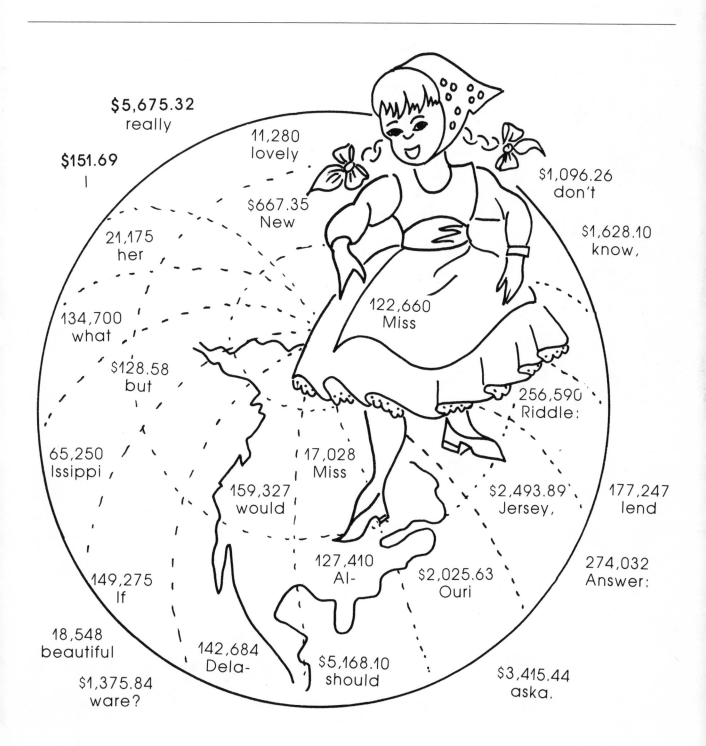

$5,675.32
really

$151.69
I

11,280
lovely

$667.35
New

$1,096.26
don't

$1,628.10
know,

21,175
her

134,700
what

122,660
Miss

$128.58
but

256,590
Riddle:

65,250
Issippi

17,028
Miss

159,327
would

$2,493.89
Jersey,

177,247
lend

127,410
Al-

$2,025.63
Ouri

274,032
Answer:

149,275
If

18,548
beautiful

142,684
Dela-

$5,168.10
should

$3,415.44
aska.

$1,375.84
ware?

Name _____

Number Fact Review (8)

Fold part A of the paper back and turn the paper over, so all you can see is column A. Study the multiplication facts in column A. When you know them, turn the paper over so you cannot see column A. See how quickly you can work the problems in column B. Unfold the paper to check your answers. Now fold column A so that it covers column B. Do the problems in column C. Unfold again to check your answers. Finally do the problems in column D and check them to finish your practice.

A

$8 \times 0 = 0$
$8 \times 1 = 8$
$8 \times 2 = 16$
$8 \times 3 = 24$
$8 \times 4 = 32$
$8 \times 5 = 40$
$8 \times 6 = 48$
$8 \times 7 = 56$
$8 \times 8 = 64$
$8 \times 9 = 72$
$8 \times 10 = 80$

---------------------- fold ----------------------

B

$8 \times 0 =$ _____
$8 \times 1 =$ _____
$8 \times 2 =$ _____
$8 \times 3 =$ _____
$8 \times 4 =$ _____
$8 \times 5 =$ _____
$8 \times 6 =$ _____
$8 \times 7 =$ _____
$8 \times 8 =$ _____
$8 \times 9 =$ _____
$8 \times 10 =$ _____

C

$8 \times 0 =$ _____
$8 \times 1 =$ _____
$8 \times 2 =$ _____
$8 \times 3 =$ _____
$8 \times 4 =$ _____
$8 \times 5 =$ _____
$8 \times 6 =$ _____
$8 \times 7 =$ _____
$8 \times 8 =$ _____
$8 \times 9 =$ _____
$8 \times 10 =$ _____

D

$8 \times 4 =$ _____
$8 \times 6 =$ _____
$8 \times 7 =$ _____
$8 \times 3 =$ _____
$8 \times 2 =$ _____
$8 \times 8 =$ _____
$8 \times 5 =$ _____
$8 \times 9 =$ _____
$8 \times 0 =$ _____
$8 \times 1 =$ _____
$8 \times 8 =$ _____

2 × 8	6 × 8	8 × 8	3 × 8	7 × 8	5 × 8
4 × 8	3 × 8	7 × 8	2 × 8	5 × 8	4 × 8
9 × 8	6 × 8	9 × 8	2 × 8	8 × 8	6 × 8
7 × 8	3 × 8	4 × 8	9 × 8	3 × 8	7 × 8
4 × 8	5 × 8	8 × 8	6 × 8	4 × 8	9 × 8
6 × 8	8 × 8	5 × 8	2 × 8	7 × 8	5 × 8
7 × 8	3 × 8	9 × 8	8 × 8	6 × 8	4 × 8

Name_____ Time _____

Use the products in columns A, B, C, D, and E to find your riddle.

	A	B	C	D	E
1	$88.79 × 8	$45.68 × 8	2,267 × 8	5,678 × 8	$98.89 × 8
2	$72.89 × 8	$46.89 × 8	3,876 × 8	6,579 × 8	41,659 × 8
3	$88.95 × 8	9,878 × 8	9,876 × 8	28,897 × 8	$489.79 × 8
4	$42.37 × 8	$876.95 × 8	$721.97 × 8	4,698 × 8	$478.62 × 8
5	48,897 × 8	$748.95 × 8	$623.78 × 8	42,869 × 8	$397.88 × 8

Name_____

Name

Use the products in columns A, B, C, D, and E to find your riddle.

	A	B	C	D	E
1	82,971 × 8	$457.62 × 8	$307.89 × 8	43,769 × 8	88,789 × 8
2	87,869 × 8	$80.65 × 8	77,981 × 8	$839.78 × 8	$879.32 × 8
3	$878.45 × 8	39,752 × 8	$688.71 × 8	42,429 × 8	$677.51 × 8
4	64,675 × 8	$738.21 × 8	$746.29 × 8	88,879 × 8	$849.87 × 8
5	$487.78 × 8	97,862 × 8	86,889 × 8	$976.83 × 8	76,549 × 8

Name＿＿＿＿＿＿＿＿＿＿＿＿＿＿＿＿＿＿＿＿＿＿＿＿＿

350,152
know

$6,798.96
Thanksgiving?

517,400
and

$5,970.32
ready

711,032
for

318,016
only

$2,463.12
you

$645.20
fat

663,768
Riddle:

$5,905.68
not

782,896
It

$7,814.64
a goblin

$3,902.24
Answer:

339,432
for

702,952
the

695,112
was

$7,034.56
turkey

$7,027.60
was

$6,718.24
Day

710,312
why

$5,420.08
Halloween

$3,660.96
Do

$5,509.68
ready

612,392
(a gobblin')

623,848
Thanksgiving

Name

Use the products in columns A, B, C, D, and E to find your riddle.

	A	B	C	D	E
1	$76.39 × 8	$88.97 × 6	5,276 × 7	8,879 × 8	6,897 × 6
2	5,898 × 7	$76.39 × 6	8,879 × 7	$187.96 × 8	$986.75 × 7
3	5,276 × 8	5,898 × 6	$76.39 × 7	5,276 × 6	$986.75 × 8
4	$489.72 × 8	6,897 × 7	$986.75 × 6	$88.97 × 8	$187.96 × 6
5	$88.97 × 7	5,898 × 8	8,879 × 6	$187.96 × 7	6,897 × 8

Name_____

68

Riddle:

$711.76 not

$534.73 He

$611.12 Why

47,184 up

$458.34 past

53,274 the

71,032 Freddy

31,656 wanted

48,279 very

55,176 pills.

41,382 tiptoe

35,388 Answer:

$622.79 wake

36,932 Foolish

41,286 quietly

62,153 the

42,208 cabinet?

$1,127.76 to

$533.82 did

$3,917.76 be

$1,503.68 doctor's

$5,920.50 careful

$6,907.25 medicine

$1,315.72 sleeping

$7,894.00 to

Name

Number Fact Review (9)

Fold part A of the paper back and turn the paper over, so all you can see is column A. Study the multiplication facts in column A. When you know them, turn the paper over so you cannot see column A. See how quickly you can work the problems in column B. Unfold the paper to check your answers. Now fold column A so that it covers column B. Do the problems in column C. Unfold again to check your answers. Finally do the problems in column D and check them to finish your practice.

A

$9 \times 0 = 0$

$9 \times 1 = 9$

$9 \times 2 = 18$

$9 \times 3 = 27$

$9 \times 4 = 36$

$9 \times 5 = 45$

$9 \times 6 = 54$

$9 \times 7 = 63$

$9 \times 8 = 72$

$9 \times 9 = 81$

$9 \times 10 = 90$

— — — — — — — — — — — — fold — — — — — — — — — — — —

B

$9 \times 0 =$ _____

$9 \times 1 =$ _____

$9 \times 2 =$ _____

$9 \times 3 =$ _____

$9 \times 4 =$ _____

$9 \times 5 =$ _____

$9 \times 6 =$ _____

$9 \times 7 =$ _____

$9 \times 8 =$ _____

$9 \times 9 =$ _____

$9 \times 10 =$ _____

....

C

$9 \times 0 =$ _____

$9 \times 1 =$ _____

$9 \times 2 =$ _____

$9 \times 3 =$ _____

$9 \times 4 =$ _____

$9 \times 5 =$ _____

$9 \times 6 =$ _____

$9 \times 7 =$ _____

$9 \times 8 =$ _____

$9 \times 9 =$ _____

$9 \times 10 =$ _____

D

$9 \times 7 =$ _____

$9 \times 4 =$ _____

$9 \times 6 =$ _____

$9 \times 3 =$ _____

$9 \times 2 =$ _____

$9 \times 8 =$ _____

$9 \times 5 =$ _____

$9 \times 9 =$ _____

$9 \times 0 =$ _____

$9 \times 1 =$ _____

$9 \times 3 =$ _____

4 × 9	6 × 9	8 × 9	9 × 9	3 × 9	7 × 9
5 × 9	7 × 9	2 × 9	5 × 9	8 × 9	9 × 9
4 × 9	6 × 9	8 × 9	5 × 9	4 × 9	7 × 9
6 × 9	3 × 9	9 × 9	4 × 9	3 × 9	7 × 9
6 × 9	8 × 9	2 × 9	9 × 9	6 × 9	9 × 9
4 × 9	5 × 9	2 × 9	7 × 9	3 × 9	4 × 9
5 × 9	7 × 9	3 × 9	8 × 9	6 × 9	2 × 9

Name _____ Time _____

Use the products in columns A, B, C, D, and E to find your riddle.

	A	B	C	D	E
1	9,091 × 9	8,789 × 9	6,787 × 9	3,089 × 9	4,879 × 9
2	9,988 × 9	7,869 × 9	9,876 × 9	4,869 × 9	9,899 × 9
3	8,765 × 9	$48.95 × 9	$98.87 × 9	$96.68 × 9	9,765 × 9
4	8,997 × 9	9,979 × 9	$99.85 × 9	8,765 × 9	$876.91 × 9
5	9,975 × 9	$187.98 × 9	3,956 × 9	4,874 × 9	$965.72 × 9

Name _____

Riddle:

$7,892.19
Answer:

79,101
did

88,884
other

89,811
of

$440.55
hen

89,892
to

43,821
chick

78,885
the

$788.85
egg?

43,866
orange

43,911
say

27,801
chick

35,604
the

61,083
one

87,885
orange

70,821
the

$898.65
an

$870.12
an

81,819
What

89,091
after

$1,691.82
at

80,973
instead

89,775
Look

$889.83
laid

$8,691.48
marmalade.

Name_____

Use the products in columns A, B, C, D, and E to find your riddle.

	A	B	C	D	E
1	82,971 × 9	$457.62 × 9	$307.89 × 9	43,769 × 9	88,789 × 9
2	$878.45 × 9	39,752 × 9	$688.71 × 9	42,429 × 9	$677.51 × 9
3	87,869 × 9	$80.65 × 9	77,981 × 9	$839.78 × 9	$879.32 × 9
4	64,675 × 9	$738.21 × 9	$746.29 × 9	88,879 × 9	$849.87 × 9
5	$487.78 × 9	97,862 × 9	86,889 × 9	$876.83 × 9	76,549 × 9

Name _____

Riddle:

Use the products in columns A, B, C, D, and E to find your riddle.

	A	B	C	D	E
1	$869.72 × 6	57,821 × 7	$987.89 × 8	$878.95 × 9	$578.21 × 6
2	$897.89 × 7	$878.95 × 6	$147.88 × 9	$992.86 × 8	$187.88 × 7
3	$878.95 × 8	$992.86 × 9	$987.89 × 6	$869.72 × 7	57,821 × 8
4	45,788 × 9	$869.72 × 8	$878.95 × 7	$147.88 × 6	$987.89 × 9
5	57,821 × 6	$992.86 × 7	$147.88 × 8	$869.72 × 9	45,788 × 8

Name _____

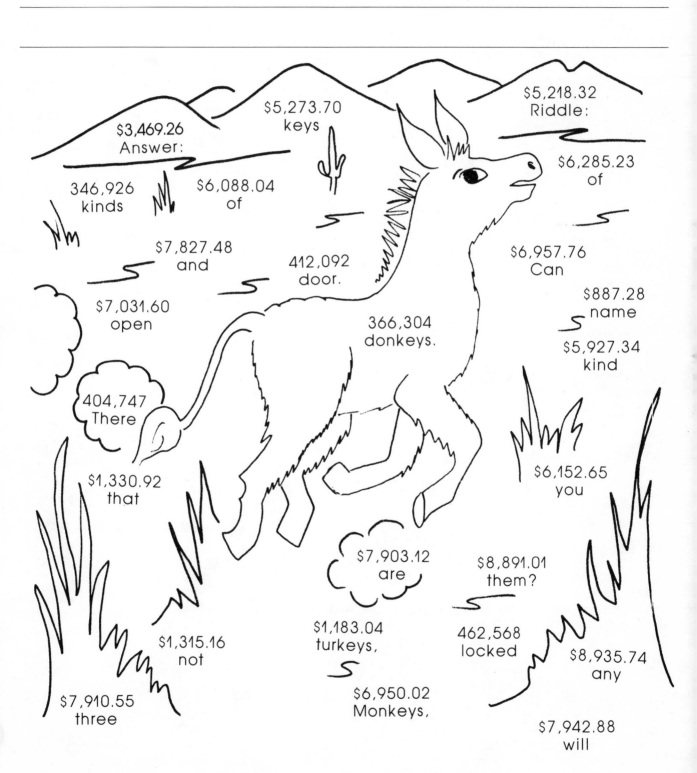

$3,469.26
Answer:

$5,273.70
keys

$5,218.32
Riddle:

346,926
kinds

$6,088.04
of

$6,285.23
of

$7,827.48
and

412,092
door.

$6,957.76
Can

$7,031.60
open

$887.28
name

366,304
donkeys.

$5,927.34
kind

404,747
There

$6,152.65
you

$1,330.92
that

$7,903.12
are

$8,891.01
them?

$1,315.16
not

$1,183.04
turkeys,

462,568
locked

$8,935.74
any

$7,910.55
three

$6,950.02
Monkeys,

$7,942.88
will

Name_____

ANSWER SHEETS

ANSWER SHEETS

Set 1

	A	B	C
1	70	158	172
2	210	224	816
3	852	1,606	870
4	1,240	444	416
5	1,196	946	404
6	642	476	600

Time Test (3)

21	18	27	12	18	15
24	9	24	6	18	0
27	12	15	21	12	24
27	18	24	6	27	15
21	27	24	21	9	27
12	18	21	9	27	15
24	18	12	27	9	18

Time Test (2)

2	12	4	10	8	0
6	4	18	12	16	14
18	10	14	16	12	0
4	16	10	18	6	12
14	18	2	8	16	6
8	16	12	18	14	10
0	18	8	10	16	6

Set 2

	A	B	C
1	850	1,662	1,246
2	1,654	1,106	1,308
3	1,950	872	1,524
4	684	1,728	1,062
5	698	1,558	1,334
6	1,170	946	450

Set 3

	A	B	C
1	105	222	243
2	285	258	171
3	138	291	264
4	303	1,815	1,221
5	2,109	2,427	1,200
6	786	885	1,053

Set 4

	A	B	C
1	1,806	1,242	2,460
2	1,389	2,655	2,727
3	2,091	1,224	999
4	2,406	2,964	618
5	2,940	2,061	1,713
6	2,274	2,706	3,021

Set 5

	A	B	C
1	2,019	1,452	1,857
2	1,179	1,746	2,424
3	2,202	2,691	1,080
4	537	2,427	1,911
5	1,116	2,751	2,286
6	693	2,268	840

Set 6

	A	B	C	D	E
1	864	1,658	2,295	696	2,388
2	1,592	1,728	1,296	1,044	854
3	1,862	2,487	1,530	1,281	2,592
4	5,580	9,242	17,302	2,262	6,963
5	3,393	10,863	3,720	25,953	4,642

20	4	28	8	36	20
32	12	20	28	32	24
36	0	32	16	36	12
24	36	12	24	0	16
28	32	20	32	28	24
36	12	16	36	28	20
16	28	36	24	32	12

Set 7

	A	B	C	D	E
1	824	1,284	844	2,816	48
2	1,360	1,848	3,348	3,664	2,472
3	3,684	840	3,992	3,144	3,284
4	1,488	1,868	4,964	3,584	8,660
5	8,316	1,588	33,164	2,900	3,540

Set 8

	A	B	C	D	E
1	1,116	3,588	2,900	3,328	3,916
2	3,304	3,728	3,024	3,316	3,988
3	21,004	34,780	30,612	30,604	37,060
4	33,188	12,084	36,448	32,048	7,060
5	38,884	13,024	13,284	39,076	22,288

Set 9

	A	B	C	D	E
1	2,956	3,316	3,624	3,284	2,660
2	39,284	30,608	22,244	12,860	38,608
3	20,324	348	25,284	27,684	34,716
4	15,060	33,104	27,748	7,304	38,092
5	33,180	30,632	12,876	34,660	17,972

Time Test (5)

35	45	30	40	30	15
40	30	25	45	15	25
45	20	5	30	45	35
40	10	0	20	40	35
10	45	30	35	45	35
0	45	40	20	5	40
45	40	15	45	35	30

Set 10

	A	B	C	D	E
1	1,876	2,619	704	7,504	12,642
2	2,312	1,408	1,407	3,752	1,734
3	25,284	5,628	3,492	1,056	1,156
4	7,588	938	18,963	1,746	22,484
5	16,863	34,760	5,871	26,070	7,828

Set 11

	A	B	C	D	E
1	$491.00	$163.80	$8.75	$11.25	$186.05
2	$99.75	$117.25	$14.10	$138.10	$1,422.35
3	$19.75	$46.85	$215.10	$86.85	$41.05
4	$67.10	$138.80	$44.20	$499.50	$26.60
5	$9.35	$21.60	$284.50	$221.60	$486.80

Set 12

	A	B	C	D	E
1	$103.75	$54.70	$39.10	$61.75	$43.70
2	$48.25	$87.45	$216.45	$284.10	$236.80
3	$1,531.05	$2,375.10	$1,988.80	$2,106.05	$238.75
4	$4,481.60	$3,631.60	$218.75	$4,606.75	$438.65
5	$214.75	$688.00	$1,623.10	$4,608.50	$214.65

Set 13

	A	B	C	D	E
1	$128.25	22,692	$139.25	$127.08	1,350
2	$139.10	3,348	1,368	$248.22	4,485
3	$211.75	$261.90	$110.48	2,439	$212.50
4	$247.92	4,650	1,278	$129.64	$412.50
5	12,591	$248.91	$170.24	$331.88	$164.75

Time Test (6)

30	42	48	36	42	18
54	24	30	48	36	54
12	42	36	54	30	0
42	48	18	48	30	42
54	36	18	12	42	24
54	30	48	36	54	48
30	42	36	18	54	48

Set 14

	A	B	C	D	E
1	2,610	4,926	2,418	372	5,022
2	2,370	1,314	5,382	2,592	4,944
3	1,836	4,170	2,622	5,358	282
4	4,974	222	5,094	2,196	4,494
5	5,292	4,524	5,190	5,838	4,956

Set 15

	A	B	C	D	E
1	$165.60	2,970	$224.52	5,382	2,922
2	$566.10	$470.70	$283.86	1,782	4,974
3	2,718	$418.56	2,796	$520.62	$203.70
4	$131.58	2,802	$219.60	2,742	4,614
5	$532.56	5,214	$226.92	$435.90	$341.88

Set 16

	A	B	C	D	E
1	2,736	$493.80	$407.70	1,254	$285.90
2	$166.20	$503.70	2,934	$560.76	$473.58
3	5,778	$509.70	$188.52	4,056	$202.08
4	$286.50	$563.22	$580.08	$443.34	5,970
5	5,022	$275.16	3,456	$299.88	$1,125.90

Set 17

	A	B	C	D	E
1	$253.56	$54.21	$233.55	$103.28	$116.22
2	$226.92	$170.10	$367.48	7,656	$978.60
3	14,427	$187.50	8,364	$109.71	12,918
4	$1,056.30	$397.71	16,375	$704.80	15,456
5	12,093	$2,195.88	$1,995.04	19,782	$1,436.91

Set 18

	A	B	C	D	E
1	2,163	1,246	3,269	5,607	441
2	5,670	3,241	6,909	2,555	6,349
3	3,234	6,153	4,235	5,586	6,846
4	5,523	4,599	5,383	6,083	3,899
5	3,486	4,823	4,963	3,409	5,439

Time Test (7)

35	28	42	35	56	49
63	49	35	56	42	21
63	28	21	56	42	63
49	35	14	42	35	28
49	21	63	0	28	49
63	35	42	56	21	63
35	56	28	42	49	14

Set 19

	A	B	C	D	E
1	$193.55	$324.24	$153.86	$328.23	3,423
2	15,386	$229.46	$622.93	$270.55	$5,584.74
3	27,139	$683.55	$5,803.00	$3,167.50	54,523
4	$622.79	61,355	27,104	$3,414.11	20,321
5	62,692	$5,513.13	$2,635.50	$2,066.40	$2,555.70

Set 20

	A	B	C	D	E
1	$4,726.47	$2,149.42	$1,948.45	$187.46	$2,748.90
2	32,347	$607.25	$6,268.92	$299.32	$1,157.24
3	$601.79	$6,760.74	30,786	$3,939.25	$223.23
4	$3,470.32	$2,680.23	$3,358.81	$3,897.04	26,747
5	$3,401.79	$2,250.92	34,104	312,074	$6,992.09

Set 21

	A	B	C	D	E
1	256,590	149,275	11,280	17,028	65,250
2	$5,168.10	177,247	122,660	$2,025.63	21,175
3	18,548	$667.35	$2,493.89	134,700	159,327
4	142,684	$1,375.84	274,032	$151.69	$1,096.26
5	$5,675.32	$1,628.10	$128.58	127,410	$3,415.44

Time Test (8)

16	48	64	24	56	40
32	24	56	16	40	32
72	48	72	16	64	48
56	24	32	72	24	56
32	40	64	48	32	72
48	64	40	16	56	40
56	24	72	64	48	32

	A	B	C	D	E
1	$710.32	$365.44	18,136	45,424	$791.12
2	$583.12	$375.12	31,008	52,632	333,272
3	$711.60	79,024	79,008	231,176	$3,918.32
4	$338.96	$7,015.60	$5,775.76	37,584	$3,828.96
5	391,176	$5,991.60	$4,990.24	342,952	$3,183.04

Set 23

	A	B	C	D	E
1	663,768	$3,660.96	$2,463.12	350,152	710,312
2	702,952	$645.20	623,848	$6,718.24	$7,034.56
3	$7,027.60	318,016	$5,509.68	339,432	$5,420.08
4	517,400	$5,905.68	$5,970.32	711,032	$6,798.96
5	$3,902.24	782,896	695,112	$7,814.64	612,392

Set 24

	A	B	C	D	E
1	$611.12	$533.82	36,932	71,032	41,382
2	41,286	$458.34	62,153	$1,503.68	$6,907.25
3	42,208	35,388	$534.73	31,656	$7,894.00
4	$3,917.76	48,279	$5,920.50	$711.76	$1,127.76
5	$622.79	47,184	53,274	$1,315.72	55,176

Time Test (9)

36	54	72	81	27	63
45	63	18	45	72	81
36	54	72	45	36	63
54	27	81	36	27	63
54	72	18	81	54	81
36	45	18	63	27	36
45	63	27	72	54	18

Set 25

	A	B	C	D	E
1	81,819	79,101	61,083	27,801	43,911
2	89,892	70,821	88,884	43,821	89,091
3	78,885	$440.55	$889.83	$870.12	87,885
4	80,973	89,811	$898.65	$788.85	$7,892.19
5	89,775	$1,691.82	35,604	43,866	$8,691.48

Set 26

	A	B	C	D	E
1	746,739	$4,118.58	277,101	393,921	799,101
2	$7,906.05	357,768	$6,198.39	381,861	$6,097.59
3	790,821	$725.85	701,829	$7,558.02	$7,913.88
4	582,075	$6,643.89	$6,716.61	799,911	$7,648.83
5	$4,390.02	880,758	782,001	$7,891.47	688,941

Set 27

	A	B	C	D	E
1	$5,218.32	404,747	$7,903.12	$7,910.55	$3,469.26
2	$6,285.23	$5,273.70	$1,330.92	$7,942.88	$1,315.16
3	$7,031.60	$8,935.74	$5,927.34	$6,088.04	462,568
4	412,092	$6,957.76	$6,152.65	$887.28	$8,891.01
5	346,926	$6,950.02	$1,183.04	$7,827.48	366,304

RIDDLE LIST

Set 1 Who is bigger, Mrs. Bigger or her darling baby boy? Answer: The darling baby is a little Bigger.

Set 2 Riddle: Why are robbers in jail called jailbirds? Answer: Because they have just been out a robbin' (a robin).

Set 3 What must you do if the baby eats your pencil? Answer: You will just have to use a pen.

Set 4 What would you call an eight-foot giant butcher who is carrying a large, sharp knife? Answer: Sir!

Set 5 Why do little pigs always eat so very much? Answer: They want to make big hogs of themselves.

Set 6 What is a skeleton? Answer: Some bones with the people scraped off. Riddle: Why didn't that skeleton cross the road? Answer: He didn't have the guts.

Set 7 What is the difference between a good moving van driver and a bad cold? Answer: One knows the stops, and the other stops the nose.

Set 8 What do you get when you cross a monster with a drip-dry suit? Answer: You are sure to get a wash-and-wear (were-) wolf.

Set 9 Riddle: Why is it always hard to get a baseball game started in the early afternoon? Answer: Because bats like to sleep in the daytime.

Set 10 Why are there walls around cemeteries? Answer: People are dying to get in, but you can only get in if you use a skeleton key.

Set 11 What did the man say when his cat was run over by a steamroller? Answer: Nothing. He just stood there with a very long puss.

Set 12 When is the weather worst for rats and mice? Answer: When it rains cats and dogs. But worse than raining cats and dogs is hailing taxicabs.

Set 13 Spell mousetrap in three letters. Answer: Cat. Riddle: Spell dried grass in three letters. Answer: Hay. Riddle: Spell hard water in three letters. Answer: Ice.

Set 14 Why can't you tell secrets on a farm? Answer: The corn has ears, the potatoes have eyes, the bean stalks, and the horses carry tails (tales).

Set 15 Riddle: Why is the very center of a large, old tree like a dog's tail? Answer: Because it is the very farthest from the bark.

Set 16 Why was General George Washington's large army so very tired on April first? Answer: Because it had just finished a long March of thirty-one days.

Set 17 Riddle: Why are traffic officers the strongest people in the whole world? Answer: Because they can hold up a five-ton truck with one hand.

Set 18 Three men fell out of their boat, but only two of the three got their hair wet. Why? Answer: Because the third man was bald.

Set 19 What is the best way to get down from a bucking horse? Answer: You don't get down from a bucking horse. You get down from a duck.

Set 20 How far can an explorer go into the jungle? Answer: He can go half way. Any further than that and he will be coming out.

Set 21 Riddle: If lovely Miss Issippi should lend Miss Ouri her beautiful New Jersey, what would Dela-ware? Answer: I don't really know, but Al-aska.

Set 22 Riddle: What does a terrible monster do when it loses one of its hands? Answer: It goes shopping in a second-hand store, of course.

Set 23 Riddle: Do you know why the fat Thanksgiving Day turkey was only ready for Halloween and not ready for Thanksgiving? Answer: It was a gobblin' (a goblin).

Set 24 Why did Foolish Freddy tiptoe quietly past the doctor's medicine cabinet? Answer: He wanted to be very careful not to wake up the sleeping pills.

Set 25 What did one chick say to the other chick after the hen laid an orange instead of an egg? Answer: Look at the orange marmalade.

Set 26 Why is an island like the letter T? Answer: Both are in the middle of water. Riddle: Why is T unhappy? Answer: It is next to U.

Set 27 Riddle: There are three kinds of keys that will not open any kind of locked door. Can you name them? Answer: Monkeys, turkeys, and donkeys.